If the Fence Could Talk

PUBLICATION MADE POSSIBLE BY THE GENEROSITY OF THE FOLLOWING:

Alfred & Judy Branch

Tom Burkhard
Todd & Dee Dobson
Jim & Christy Everest
Joel & Kristi Forhan
Hudiburg Auto Group
Richard & Pat Lawson
Ricky & Kelly Lawson with 419 Outreach
Lippert Bros., Inc.
Mary Jane Bell Maidt
Main Street Parking, LLC
Mathis Brothers Furniture
MidFirst Bank
Midtown Renaissance
The Norman Reynolds Family
Southwestern Roofing & Metal, Inc.

Jeff & Michelle Eggleston
Gerd & Lucky Fecht
Ann & Burns Hargis
Mark & Ellie Harvill
Cort Hoge
Katie Hoge
Rob & Karen Luke

Steve McCormack & Lisa Graham
Quail Creek Bank
Roofscapes Exteriors, LLC
Patty Rother
Larry & Lynda Scott
Dr. & Mrs. Michael Sellers
Ronnie, Ashley & Gracie Taylor

If the Fence Could Talk

By Brad Robison
Illustrated by Margaret Hoge

Series Editor: Gini Moore Campbell

OKLAHOMA HALL *of* FAME
OKLAHOMA HERITAGE ASSOCIATION PUBLISHING

OKLAHOMA HALL *of* FAME

2015 OFFICERS AND DIRECTORS

CHAIRMAN OF THE BOARD
Joe Moran III, Tulsa

CHAIRMAN-ELECT OF THE BOARD
Mark Stansberry, Edmond

CHAIRMAN EMERITUS OF THE BOARD
Nevyle R. Cable, Okmulgee

VICE CHAIRMEN OF THE BOARD - EC
Bruce T. Benbrook, Woodward
Stan Clark, Stillwater
Rebecca Dixon, Tulsa
Ken Fergeson, Altus
Fred Harlan, Okmulgee
Judy Hatfield, Norman
Clayton C. Taylor, Oklahoma City
Steven W. Taylor, McAlester

CORPORATE SECRETARY
Jennifer M. Grigsby, Oklahoma City

TREASURER
Bill W. Burgess, Jr., Lawton

**CHAIRMAN APPOINTMENTS
DIRECTORS AT LARGE - EC**
Clayton I. Bennett, Oklahoma City
Rhonda Hooper, Oklahoma City
Xavier Niera, Norman

PRESIDENT
Shannon L. Rich, Oklahoma City

CHAIRMEN'S COUNCIL
Calvin Anthony, Stillwater
Pat Henry, Lawton
Roxana Lorton, Tulsa
Tom McDaniel, Oklahoma City
Lee Allan Smith, Oklahoma City
G. Lee Stidham, Checotah

DIRECTORS
Phil B. Albert, Claremore
Alison Anthony, Sand Springs
Steve Burrage, Antlers
Ann Caine, Stillwater
Amanda Clinton, Tulsa
Chad Dillingham, Enid
Malinda Berry Fischer, Stillwater
Virginia G. Groendyke, Enid
Joe D. Hall, Elk City
Robert Henry, Oklahoma City
Gary Huckabay, Yukon
Kirk Jewell, Stillwater
Glen D. Johnson, Oklahoma City
Duke R. Ligon, Seminole
John Massey, Durant

John M. McArthur, Lawton
Vicki Miles-LaGrange, Oklahoma City
Gary Parker, Muskogee
Gregory E. Pyle, Durant
Richard N. Ryerson, Alva
Michael E. Smith, Oklahoma City
Renzi Stone, Oklahoma City
Kathy Taylor, Tulsa
Stratton Taylor, Claremore
Steve Turnbo, Tulsa
Michael C. Turpen, Oklahoma City
Hardy Watkins, Oklahoma City
Ronald H. White, Oklahoma City

©2015 Oklahoma Heritage Association Publishing, a publication of the Oklahoma Hall of Fame

Printed in Canada
ISBN: 978-1-938923-18-0
LIBRARY OF CONGRESS CONTROL NUMBER: 2015939182

Book and Cover Design: Skip McKinstry

Dedicated to the families, survivors, and rescue workers
whose lives were forever changed on April 19, 1995.

FOREWORD

April 19, 1995 was a day of unspeakable horror and tragedy.

Early that morning, a rental truck pulled in front of the Alfred P. Murrah Federal Building in downtown Oklahoma City. In its bed rested a fuel oil and fertilizer bomb that, when detonated, tore away the north face of the building, created a racing fire of nearby exploding automobiles, and damaged or destroyed over three hundred other buildings in the area.

This incredible and unforgivable act of one demented individual, snuffed out the lives of one hundred sixty-eight of our neighbors and friends and injured hundreds more. The bombing remains the largest criminal case in the history of the FBI (the perpetrators of 9/11 killed themselves in their act of madness so there was no one living to prosecute). The Nation's attention became focused on the rescue efforts, then the recovery efforts, and finally on the arrest and prosecution of those responsible.

From across the country, urban search and rescue workers came in the thousands. From California, Washington, Maryland, Florida, Arizona, New York, Virginia, and cities and towns in between, men and women, committed to professionalism and compassion, joined their Oklahoma colleagues at the site. What astonished them and helped create "the Oklahoma Standard," was not only the superb training and leadership of the Oklahoma first responders and their colleagues, but the kindness and the charity of the Oklahoma family. Everything that they needed or wanted was provided: food, communications, medical care, clothing. Their request was our command and it continued that way until their work was done. There was no looting. The crime rate collapsed in the city.

But there was more. Spontaneously, the chain link fence surrounding the site became the place where notes, letters of love, stuffed animals, children's toys, religious items, and assorted memorabilia came and stayed. To this day, visitors continue to mark their visits by their gifts to the "Fence."

The "Fence" has taken on a life of its own as a place of remembrance and Faith and healing.

Brad Robison tells its story with creativity and goodness and grace. His is a gifted tribute to the good that came out of the bad. It is a piece of a people at their best.

Frank Keating
Governor of Oklahoma, 1995-2003

ACKNOWLEDGMENTS

I wish to thank Tom Burkhard, Melissa Creasey, Diane Fitzimmons, Carolyn Hust, Carl Sennhenn, Thomas Brent Smith, and my cousin Greg Jones for taking time to read the manuscript and provide insightful suggestions and editorial comments.

A special thanks to Mrs. Jane Thomas for her incredible sense of history, especially as it relates to the Oklahoma City bombing and the preservation of its memory. Mrs. Thomas was the first Curator of Collections for the Oklahoma City National Memorial and Museum Archives and dedicated untold hours to arranging, organizing, and cataloging thousands of items left on the fence. Helen Stiefmiller and Pam Bell, currently of the Oklahoma City National Memorial Archive, were also invaluable in assisting me with this project.

I'm grateful for staff members of the Rose State College Learning Resources Center and especially for Rick Cochran and Janet Griffith for their technical support. I also want to thank Judi Lashley and her "Social Studies in the Elementary School" class at the University of Central Oklahoma for their support and encouragement.

For their friendship and support of this project I am indebted to former Oklahoma Governor and Mrs. Frank Keating and offer heartfelt thanks for their support.

I owe a huge debt of gratitude to Margaret Hoge for her artwork, without which the book would not adequately tell the story of the fence.

I also want to thank Gini Moore Campbell, Director of Publications and Education for Oklahoma Heritage Association Publishing and the Gaylord-Pickens Museum, home of the Oklahoma Hall of Fame, for recognizing the importance of the fence and the significance of telling its story.

And, with love and gratitude, I thank my sister Shelley Robison Hembree and my brother Dr. Craig Robison for their life-long support and encouragement.

Dr. Brad Robison

2015

If the Fence Could Talk

The fence company opened at 6:00 a.m. on April 19, 1995.

The smell of coffee filled the warehouse. The guys would always start their day with stories and several cups of that dark, hot, good smelling coffee. As I lay in the storage facility of the fence company on that beautiful spring morning, I could tell summer was just around the corner. The concrete floor on which I rested was always a little cold, but, with spring temperatures beginning to rise, the floor was warming up. Forklifts were buzzing around and workers were scurrying to get the trucks loaded for deliveries.

Spring always sees an increase in business because new homes are being completed, folks are getting ready to work outdoors, and many fences have to be repaired or even replaced after severe storms. When standing upright, I am tall. My barbs are sharp and my color is glistening silver. Although a fairly large fence, by most standards I am just a basic, chain-link fence.

When the store manager called a meeting for 9:00 a.m., the guys swallowed the last sip of their coffee, shut off the forklifts, and settled in the conference room. Still laying on the floor, I was close enough to hear voices begin to quiet as the manager strolled into the room. It was in the middle of the manager's speech that we heard a very loud boom and felt the ground beneath us shudder. The windows rattled and the doors actually bowed.

The clock on the wall said it was 9:02.

After a few seconds of silence, a warehouse employee yelled, "What was that?"

One of the other workers exclaimed, "I think it was an earthquake."

Another yelled, "No way, not an earthquake in Oklahoma. I think it was a sonic boom."

Finally, a worker who had served in the military shouted, "No! That was a bomb or some sort of explosion."

I was really scared and did not know what to do; after all, I'm just a fence and there's not much I could do. The manager quickly turned on a television near the speaker's podium, but nothing was being reported.

Somewhat dismissing the loud noise and shaking of the building, the manager turned down the television and resumed the meeting. Just a few minutes later however, one of those "Breaking News" tabs came across the screen to report something significant. There it was—a news helicopter hovering over the north side of a building downtown. About one-third of the building had been blown away. Debris was floating in the air, cars were burning, people were running, and a tree was stripped nearly bare of limbs and leaves.

None of the guys in the warehouse recognized the building at first, but when the helicopter flew to the north, someone yelled, "That is the Federal Building!"

Some men thought the destruction might have been caused by a gas explosion, while the ex-military guy continued to proclaim it had been a bomb. The sounds of emergency vehicles were now heard, and the phones began to ring. I could see the frustration on the faces of the employees when our phones went dead. Later it became clear that phone lines were being jammed by all the calls being made at the same time. I lay still on the floor of the warehouse, wondering what had happened. The forklifts remained still, and the trucks, ready to head out for the day, remained in place.

As the morning wore on, it became apparent that the loud, shaking noise was indeed a bomb and not a gas explosion. The news reporters were now saying that it was perhaps a terrorist bomb, something someone might see in the Middle East or in Northern Ireland. All the folks in the warehouse seemed nervous when there were reports that the governor had shut down state offices and the National Guard had been called out. There were calls for off duty doctors and nurses to report downtown and donors to donate blood for numerous casualties. As the news spread throughout the city, people everywhere turned on their televisions. Some were desperate to know the fate of family members who might have been in the building. Others wanted to know about relatives in the area. Many simply wanted to know what was going on. Televisions had identified the building as the Alfred P. Murrah Federal Building.

Feelings of despair, sadness, and shock were evident on the faces of everyone in the warehouse. As for me, I remained scared, nervous, and confused. How could such a thing happen in the heartland of America? How could someone deliberately blow up a United States Federal Building with innocent men, women, and children inside? The Federal Building had housed a day care center for children of Federal employees; an idea that had been established in the 1970's to attract potential workers. News spread rapidly throughout the city, the state, and the nation. President Bill Clinton was notified of the horrific crime that had been committed in Oklahoma City and promised the nation to deliver remarks later in the day. U.S. Attorney General Janet Reno also planned to speak to the nation about what was being done by the law enforcement community.

Since 9:02 a.m. emergency personnel and ordinary citizens had been running into the Alfred P. Murrah Federal Building to lend their assistance. Nearly an hour and a half had passed and at 10:30, the news showed people running away from the building. I then heard one of the employees of the warehouse say that another bomb had been discovered. People were running and running quickly. I could hear the nervousness of the reporters. More bombs: run, everyone run.

It took time for the building to be declared clear of other bombs. Once the go-ahead was given, work continued taking out the injured and removing those that did not survive.

Hours passed and still our forklifts and trucks did not move. I could see a great deal of anticipation on the faces of the employees, but no one seemed to know what we were waiting for, and most seemed clueless about what to do. As the day wore on, the sky became dark. Then there was a loud boom of thunder announcing a typical, spring-time Oklahoma thunderstorm. The winds began to howl and the tree limbs I could see through the warehouse window were bending in different directions. The rain was pouring, and those poor rescue workers were getting drenched; the building became more dangerous to work in. There was talk of possible collapse as debris continued to fall. Filing cabinets, computers, tables, chairs, cash from the credit union, and many other items were flying out of the building and onto the workers below. There were now calls for flashlights, blankets, gloves, and food. Rescue dogs were being brought in, and their paws were cut by the jagged concrete, glass, and rebar. There were calls for more help and for booties for the dogs and socks for the rescuers. I also heard a call for generators because the power was out, and workers needed to pump water out of what was the basement of the building. Water lines had been destroyed, as well as gas and electric lines. With the rain and strong wind, nothing seemed to be getting better.

Suddenly there was a pause on the television. A quiet fell over the warehouse. I strained to hear and discovered that the President was about to speak. Of course, I could hear only bits and pieces, but I did hear him mention the word "cowards." He promised whoever had done this would be caught and brought to justice. After the President, the Attorney General promised the nation that everything possible would be done to apprehend the "terrorists." Unknown to anyone speaking from Washington, the culprit was already in an Oklahoma jail. Yes, according to local reports a day or two later, a young man had been pulled over by the Oklahoma Highway Patrol for speeding with no license tag. In his possession was a gun.

By the next morning, the rain had stopped, clouds were beginning to break, and the sun began to peek through; I was glad to see it. The workers in the warehouse were trying to get back into the swing of things, but it was not easy. The entire nation was focused on Oklahoma City and the search and recovery. By now, the world knew that a children's day care was on the second floor of the bombed out building. One picture that was on the front page of nearly every newspaper in the world showed the limp body of a little girl being carried out of the rubble by one of the many rescue workers. In all, nineteen children had been killed, and a dozen more injured.

Many poignant stories came out of the first hours and days following the bombing, one of which I heard months later.

Rescuers worked night and day sifting through rubble and debris looking for the dead and injured. During the process of the search and recovery someone noticed a lone figure standing near the base of the building night after night, sometimes even in the rain. It was later determined that the figure was Governor Frank Keating, waiting and watching and hoping for survivors.

Another story I heard was of a rescue worker finding a teddy bear and a bouquet of flowers that had been placed carefully near Ground Zero. Not wanting to disturb the teddy bear and flowers, the rescue worker simply took note of them and continued his search for victims. Stories such as these were shared by the dozens.

The hours turned into days, and the days turned into weeks. For the first several days, what was left of the building after the bombing was guarded by the National Guard. You see, it was not only hallowed ground where many had been killed; it was still a search site and a crime scene. The area extended for blocks. One morning one of our delivery trucks backed up to the loading dock of the warehouse. I heard the usual voices of the guys working there, but then there was a voice I had not heard before. I could not see who was speaking, but I did see the letters FBI on his jacket. The man and some of our guys looked around the warehouse floor. I was not sure why.

I wanted to help, but I am just an ordinary chain-link fence!

I was also nervous and scared. When the men were practically standing right on top of me, the FBI guy said, "This is the one for us." Within a few short minutes, I was being scooped up by one of the forklifts and loaded into the back of a delivery truck. Although I was unaware of what was in store for me, I felt it might be something important. The truck bounced through the streets of Oklahoma City. After about 20 minutes, the truck came to a stop. I heard more strange voices and could see several serious faces, lots of broken glass, small and large chunks of concrete, and weary firefighters. I realized we were at the site of the bombing. There were more strange voices and before I knew it, I was being pulled out of the back of the truck and laid on the ground. The sky was blue, the color of the Oklahoma flag. The wind was brisk, and the sound of jackhammers and drills could be heard in the background. Then, I was carried to a side street just north of the site. Not knowing what was planned, I grew more restless and scared. Several workers began to unroll me and prepare me. My links were stretched onto posts that are used to help a fence stand upright. It is a good thing I am strong because it became apparent to me that I was replacing the National Guard as the guardian of this sacred site. Once the posts were secured to the ground, I was placed in an upright position.

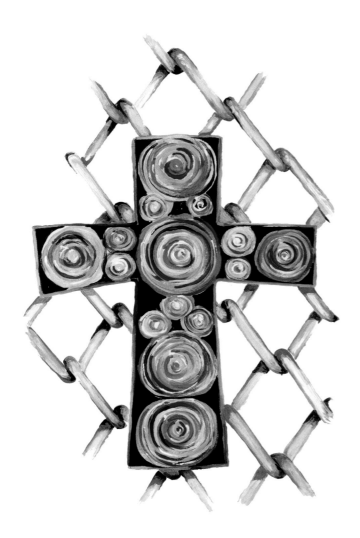

My long vigil had begun.

At first I stood silent, somewhat nervous, always wondering if I was up to the task. Could I guard the crime scene and yet help maintain a reverence that should always be present at this site? Could I be resilient and tough enough to watch all the visitors who might walk by my side? Could I withstand the Oklahoma wind, rain, and hail? I knew that the answers to these questions would come in time, but, for now, I was simply content to be what I later heard myself called: THE FENCE. I stretched for many blocks because the damage and possible evidence had been blown long distances. I wrapped around what was the Journal Record Building at 6th Street and down Harvey Avenue to 4th Street. I then turned back to the east, headed towards Robinson Avenue, and finally back up to 6th Street. Yes, I was quite a sight to behold if I do say so myself. I was shiny and stood up straight just like a soldier. I had a couple of gates attached to me in various locations so that search-and-rescue workers could enter and leave without problems. Those gates also allowed in law enforcement folks busy sifting through tons of debris and broken buildings. In all, something like fourteen buildings were destroyed, and hundreds were damaged. Glass still shimmered on the ground, and burned-out cars remained under the large American elm tree, just south of the Journal Record Building.

After all of my sections were connected, the site of the bombing was now secure and ready for the curious to pass by. Sometime late at night, another rescue worker, finding the teddy bear and flowers at Ground Zero, gently picked them up and attached them to my side. Apparently the teddy bear had been placed at Ground Zero by an Oklahoma City Firefighter and his son early one morning during the initial response to the bombing. I was told it had been a touching sight, as the firefighter and his son left the bear, hugged each other, and offered a prayer. This was the beginning of a memorial that will never be forgotten.

The next day people began to stroll by and peer through the slots in my side. Many wept openly as many more tied yellow ribbons to my links and posts. Some placed American flags on my sides, while others left flowers and stuffed animals. Some folks tied T-shirts to my links while others attached ball caps, a baseball bat, dolls, and even automobile license plates. One morning I awoke to find golf clubs leaning against one of my many sections. Before long I was nearly covered with items from all over the world, including posters, poems, and photos, from loved ones. Anything you can imagine was left at my feet or tied to my thousands of chain links: handkerchiefs, crosses, Stars of David, and Native American Dream Catchers both small and large.

One sunny afternoon in the middle of the summer, a car drove along my side.

An older gentleman struggled to get out of the car and into a wheel-chair assisted by a friend or family member. He held a piece of cardboard in his hand. He rolled up to one of my sides and affixed the cardboard to me. Although I could not hear everything the man said, I did hear, "This should not happen on our own soil, by one of our own." Of course, he was referring to the fact that, shortly after the blast, a Highway Patrol trooper had stopped a speeding car, one without a license tag. Though not known at the time, it was later discovered that the driver of that car was a former American military man who had caused this tragedy. The legless man in the wheel chair wheeled himself back towards the street, and his friend helped him struggle back into the car. After some days had gone by, one of the volunteers helping to save items tied to my links discovered the piece of cardboard with a Purple Heart attached along with the words, "I lost both my legs in Vietnam, and the people of Oklahoma need this more than I do," and signed, "A Texan who served his country."

Months turned to years, the elm tree, known today as the Survivor Tree, sprouted new limbs. A sprinkler system was installed to water it during the dry months. As for me, I stood strong as thousands and thousands of people strolled by my side. The rubble had been cleared, the shattered glass was no longer visible, and talk of a memorial could be heard throughout the area. On a cool October day, I saw many men and women approaching me in black suits with strange small buttons attached to their coats. I was reminded of that first anniversary when President Bill Clinton and his wife, First Lady Hillary Clinton, visited the site to leave wreaths in memory of those who had been killed. The people with the black coats and strange pins on their jackets had been there that day, too, and now more were here, pouring out of big black cars. Shiny shovels were handed to some of these people as more and more visitors arrived. A great number of media representatives were setting up cameras and sound equipment. Then almost out of nowhere, a large black limo pulled up and out hopped more people in black suits. To my surprise one of those people was the Vice President of the United States, Al Gore, with his wife Tipper, who had come to break ground for the Oklahoma City National Memorial.

One late September day, an unusually large crowd began to gather near me.

I was unsure what was going to happen, but in the crowd were some of the fellows I used to see in the fence warehouse several years ago. They were carrying large steel wire cutters and began cutting some of the wires holding me to the posts. When a number of the wires had been cut, several hundred people lifted me up and began to move me towards Harvey Avenue on the west side of the site. I am sure I was quite heavy because of the hundreds of items still attached to my sides. The group stood me upright and started to reattach me to posts already cemented in the ground. This was to be my new home, the Oklahoma City National Memorial, and my permanent place in history. There had been discussion about removing me completely from the site, but family members, rescuers, and survivors wanted me to stay. I overheard a lady say, "The fence is America's Hallmark Card to us." The designers of the new Memorial had been selected and they suggested that I be placed near the 9:03 gate at the west end of the Memorial. You see, 9:03 was the moment right after the blast, in other words, the first moment of healing. What better place to put me than near the symbolic area of healing?

I would experience many sad moments as well as tremendously happy moments over the next several years.

People strolled by me at all hours of the day and night. Some shed tears. Some came in large groups, while others came alone. Many stayed for long periods of time, just staring at me and asking the same question over and over: How could someone blow up a building with innocent men, women, and children inside? Business cards were left by the thousands, not in an attempt to promote business but to leave words of encouragement. One particularly poignant time, a woman approached me with a large hand-woven wreath decorated with beautiful ribbons and trinkets. Three things attached to the wreath really caught my attention. A photo of a very attractive young woman wearing a stylish hat was carefully clipped to the top of the wreath; on one side of the wreath was what looked to be the same hat as in the photo. At the bottom of the wreath was something even more interesting: a tube of lipstick. As the woman carefully attached the wreath to me, she wept ever so quietly. I found out later she was the mother of the young lady in the photograph who had been killed in the bombing. In dealing with her grief, she went through her daughter's bedroom pulling out hats and lipstick tubes for which her daughter was well-known by friends. Strangers could look at the photo and immediately understand that the young lady in the photo dressed with flashy hats and wore bright lipstick. Wreaths honoring the life of that beautiful young lady are still attached to me today.

Shortly after the groundbreaking by Vice President Al Gore, the rumble of bulldozers, jack hammers, and cranes could be heard. Tons of soil was removed from what used to be 5th Street, and truck load after truck load of debris from the bombed-out buildings left the site. As construction continued, people still strolled by me in absolute amazement that this memorial would long be standing in remembrance of 168 lives lost in the deadliest act of domestic terrorism in U.S. History.

Every anniversary of the bombing I witness the solemn ceremony commemorating the event. More flags, wreaths, and mementos are pinned to my sides. The day after the fourth anniversary something changed. People walked more quietly and reflectively than usual. Tears were shed and prayers were offered. I heard people quietly speak of Columbine High School in Colorado and a shooting that had left fifteen people dead. The date was April 20, 1999. Months later a bus pulled up beside me and young adults poured out of the bus onto the sidewalk. A large white banner was carried towards me. I could see the intent was to pin that banner somewhere on my many links. In bold letters the banner proclaimed their understanding. Students from Columbine High School then lifted the banner and secured it to me.

People from around the globe began to view the Oklahoma City National Memorial as a place to remember and honor their loved ones.

As a permanent fixture of the Memorial I beamed with pride as people strolled by twenty four hours a day and three hundred sixty-five days a year.

As the fifth anniversary drew near, there was hustle and bustle about getting the memorial ready for its official dedication. The President came, as did the First Lady, in addition to other important dignitaries. President Clinton cut the ribbon, a military band performed patriotic music, and Scottish bagpipers blew the strains of "Amazing Grace." Air Force jets flew over in remembrance of all the victims. At 9:02 a.m. on April 19, 2000, the Oklahoma City National Memorial was officially dedicated. President and Mrs. Clinton led a group of survivors and family members to the holy ground, surprised by how much peace, comfort, and hope the Memorial brought to them. It is a remarkable Memorial, with the bronze gates of time, the empty chairs that rest on the former footprint of the Alfred P. Murrah Federal Building, the Survivor Tree standing majestically and guarding the site and, of course, the children's area honoring and remembering the nineteen children who lost their lives that April morning. The hundreds who survived are beautifully honored on large, granite plaques in the "Survivors Chapel."

Entering the grounds of the Memorial, many famous people have strolled past me. Sarah, Duchess of York, a member of the British Royal Family, has been by me several times, each time leaving some remembrance. One time she even played ring around the rosy around the base of the Survivor Tree with children who had survived the blast. President and Mrs. George W. Bush, Rudy Giuliani, Janet Reno, members of the U.S. Congress, nearly every member of the NBA, and dignitaries from all over the world—all have come.

I became very close friends with many people who lost a loved one in the bombing. Some visited me on a regular basis. One of those who came regularly had lost her young, pregnant daughter. Her daughter had come to work that morning in the federal building and was showing her newly acquired ultrasound photos. As I listened closely I heard my friend explain to a visitor, she and her daughter were best friends and went shopping nearly every week together. When my friend was at work that morning, she saw a picture of the bombed-out building and immediately recognized it as the building in which her daughter worked. She quickly hurried downtown amidst the fears that would soon become a reality. Her daughter and her daughter's unborn son had perished. Today, when you walk past me and into the field of empty chairs, you will see three chairs that have two names on them. Those chairs represent the pregnant women and their unborn children. The chair shared by my friend's daughter and her unborn son are among those chairs.

More years passed without any hint of tragedy, and then came September 2001.

It was another one of those beautiful mornings when people were going about their lives, working, playing, studying, a day like any other day. At first, there was the numbness on the streets near where I stood. An eerie silence. Then there were people and more people—all leaving little American flags on me. There were more tears, more teddy bears, and more expressions of fear and anger. Later that day, I heard the news that planes had crashed into the World Trade Center in New York, and other planes flew into the Pentagon and an open field in Pennsylvania. As I continue to stand over 168 empty chairs, memorializing those lost on April 19, 1995, I remind people to contemplate violence, its causes, and consequences.

Will this violence ever stop?

Will I ever be empty of items attached to my sides? Will comfort, strength, peace, hope, and serenity ever mark this site that I stand so close to? We can all only pray that some day that will happen. In the meantime I will stand proud, for those who were killed, those who survived, those who assisted in the search, rescue, and recovery, and those whose lives were forever changed.

Bibliography

Newspapers
The Oklahoman

Collections
Oklahoma City National Memorial and Museum, Archives

Books
Simple Truths: The Real Story of the Oklahoma City Bombing Investigation